HI! I AM YOUR BABY

D1451619

THIS BOOK IS A WORK OF FICTION. THE NAMES, CHARACTERS AND EVENTS IN THIS BOOK ARE THE PRODUCTS OF THE AUTHOR'S IMAGINATION OR ARE USED FICTITIOUSLY. ANY SIMILARITY TO REAL PERSONS LIVING OR DEAD IS COINCIDENTAL AND NOT INTENDED BY THE AUTHOR.

HI! I AM YOUR BABY

PUBLISHED BY GATEKEEPER PRESS

2167 STRINGTOWN RD, SUITE 109

COLUMBUS, OH 43123-2989

WWW.GATEKEEPERPRESS.COM

COPYRIGHT © 2019 BY REBECCA UNGER, M.D.; EMILY FISHMAN, ILLUSTRATOR

ALL RIGHTS RESERVED. NEITHER THIS BOOK, NOR ANY PARTS WITHIN IT MAY BE SOLD OR REPRODUCED IN ANY FORM OR BY ANY ELECTRONIC OR MECHANICAL MEANS, INCLUDING INFORMATION STORAGE AND RETRIEVAL SYSTEMS WITHOUT PERMISSION IN WRITING FROM THE AUTHOR. THE ONLY EXCEPTION IS BY A REVIEWER, WHO MAY QUOTE SHORT EXCERPTS IN A REVIEW.

ISBN (PAPERBACK): 9781642377286

PRINTED IN THE UNITED STATES OF AMERICA

TO MOM/GRAMMA MAX, WHO TAUGHT US THE BEAUTY OF FAMILY MEALS, FAMILY GATHERINGS, AND PICKING WILDFLOWERS

TO OUR FAMILY, WHOM WE LOVE TO THE MOON, AROUND THE WORLD, AND BACK INFINITY TIMES

TO MY PATIENTS, WHO HAVE BEEN TEACHING AND INSPIRING ME FOR MANY, MANY YEARS —R.U.

HI. I AM YOUR BABY!
I AM READY TO GO ON THIS
JOURNEY.

I LEARN AND LEARN FROM THE
WORLD AROUND ME.
I LOVE MY LULLABIES AND A
GOOD STORY.

MY SLEEPING PATTERNS WILL BE JUST WHAT IS RIGHT FOR MY FAMILY AND ME.

SHORT NAPS AT FIRST, AND THEN LONGER ONES, YOU WILL SEE. THE MORE RESTED I AM, THE BETTER I WILL ...ZZZZZZZ.

FEED ME, PLAY WITH ME, TAKE ME
FOR A STROLL.

FAMILY MEALTIME IS EVENTUALLY
THE GOAL.

TUMMY TIME FROM THE
BEGINNING IS HOW I ROLL.
YOU ARE MY ROLE MODEL
FOR LIFE AS A WHOLE.

AROUND THE BLOCK WE WILL GO,
ADVENTURES NEAR AND FAR,
SHARING AS I GROW.

WE WILL TAKE STEPS TOGETHER
AND THEN — WHOA!
YOU WILL LAUNCH ME TO STEP OUT
ON MY OWN, YOU KNOW.

WE WILL HELP EACH OTHER AS
FAMILIES DO.

OUR PATH WILL HAVE CIRCLES,
ZIG ZAGS, ON LAND OR CANOE.

WE WILL ROLL DOWN A HILLSIDE
AND PICK WILDFLOWERS TOO.
IT'S ALL ABOUT LOVE BETWEEN
ME AND YOU.

ABOUT US

REBECCA UNGER (AUTHOR, MOM) IS A PEDIATRICIAN WITH THE NORTHWESTERN CHILDREN'S PRACTICE AND AN ASSOCIATE PROFESSOR OF CLINICAL PEDIATRICS AT NORTHWESTERN UNIVERSITY FEINBERG SCHOOL OF MEDICINE. SHE ENJOYS WORKING WITH FAMILIES TO HELP THEM DEVELOP HEALTHY PATTERNS AND HABITS FROM INFANCY THROUGH ADOLESCENCE AND YOUNG ADULTHOOD.

EMILY FISHMAN (ILLUSTRATOR, DAUGHTER) IS A FASHION DESIGNER AND SEMI—PROFESSIONAL DOODLER. SHE ENJOYS EXPERIMENTING WITH VARIOUS ART FORMS, INCLUDING GRAPHIC DESIGN, OIL AND WATERCOLOR PAINTING, SKETCHING, AND, OF COURSE, SEWING.

THE NORTHWESTERN CHILDREN'S PRACTICE (NWCP) TEAM EDUCATES PARENTS TO HELP THEM RAISE HEALTHY CHILDREN AND EDUCATES CHILDREN TO HELP THEM DEVELOP HEALTHY HABITS. FOUNDED IN 1973, THE NWCP PROVIDES COMPREHENSIVE CARE WITH INDIVIDUALIZED ATTENTION FOR CHILDREN FROM INFANCY THROUGH ADOLESCENCE.

VISIT THE WEBSITE FOR MORE INFORMATION:

WWW.NWCPPEDIATRICS.COM.

A NOTE TO PARENTS

THE AMERICAN ACADEMY OF PEDIATRICS PROMOTES READING ALOUD TO CHILDREN, BEGINNING IN INFANCY TO ENHANCE EARLY LITERACY SKILLS, IMPROVE SCHOOL READINESS AND TO STRENGTHEN THE RELATIONSHIP BETWEEN PARENTS AND CHILDREN DURING THIS CRITICAL TIME IN A DEVELOPING BRAIN. READING TOGETHER ALSO SUPPORTS THE BUILDING BLOCKS THAT LAUNCH A YOUNG CHILD'S LANGUAGE AND SOCIAL EMOTIONAL SKILLS FOR A LIFETIME.

WE ENCOURAGE PARENTS AND FAMILIES TO FOLLOW THE "5 R'S" OF EARLY BRAIN AND CHILD DEVELOPMENT, AS DESCRIBED BY THE AMERICAN ACADEMY OF PEDIATRICS REPORT, "EARLY EDUCATION: THE 5 R'S".

READ TOGETHER AS A DAILY FUN FAMILY ACTIVITY.

RHYME, PLAY, TALK, SING, AND CUDDLE TOGETHER EVERY DAY.

DEVELOP **R**OUTINES, ESPECIALLY FOR MEALS, PLAY, SLEEP, AND FAMILY FUN.

REWARD YOUR CHILD WITH PRAISE FOR SUCCESSES TO BUILD SELF—ESTEEM AND ENCOURAGE POSITIVE BEHAVIOR.

DEVELOP A STRONG AND NURTURING **R**ELATIONSHIP WITH YOUR CHILD AS A FOUNDATION FOR HEALTHY DEVELOPMENT.

ADAPTED FROM:

COUNCIL ON EARLY CHILDHOOD, LITERACY PROMOTION: AN ESSENTIAL COMPONENT OF PRIMARY CARE PEDIATRIC PRACTICE.

HTTPS://PEDIATRICS.AAPPUBLICATIONS.ORG/CONTENT/134/2/404

EARLY EDUCATION: THE 5 R'S. AMERICAN ACADEMY OF PEDIATRICS.

HTTPS://WWW.AAP.ERG/EN—US/ADVOCACY—AND—POLICY/AAP—HEALTH—INITIATIVES/EBCD/PAGES/FIVE.ASPX

HTTPS://WWW.NWCPPEDIATRICS.COM/